Scholastic Success With

BRAIN PLAY™

4th–6th Grade

Workbook

NEW YORK • TORONTO • LONDON • AUCKLAND • SYDNEY
MEXICO CITY • NEW DELHI • HONG KONG • BUENOS AIRES

Acknowledgments

From *SCHOLASTIC SUCCESS WITH MATH WORKBOOK*, Grade 5. Published by
Scholastic Professional Books/Scholastic Inc. Copyright © 2002 by
Scholastic Inc. Reprinted with permission.

From *SCHOLASTIC SUCCESS WITH READING WORKBOOK*, Grade 5. Published by
Scholastic Professional Books/Scholastic Inc. Copyright © 2002 by
Scholastic Inc. Reprinted with permission.

From *SCHOLASTIC SUCCESS WITH WRITING WORKBOOK*, Grade 5. Published by
Scholastic Professional Books/Scholastic Inc. Copyright © 2002 by
Scholastic Inc. Reprinted with permission.

From *SCHOLASTIC SUCCESS WITH GRAMMAR WORKBOOK*, Grade 5. Published by
Scholastic Professional Books/Scholastic Inc. Copyright © 2002 by
Scholastic Inc. Reprinted with permission.

From *SCHOLASTIC SUCCESS WITH: CHARTS, TABLES AND GRAPHS* by Michael
Priestly. Copyright © 2002 by Michael Priestly.
Used by permission of Scholastic Teaching Resources, Scholastic Inc.

Cover art by Bob Masheris
Cover design by Anna Christian
Interior illustrations by Elizabeth Adams, Jon Buller, Susan Hendron,
Reggie Holladay, Anne Kennedy, Kathy Marlin, and Bob Masheris
Interior design by Quack & Company

ISBN 0-439-82362-5

2 3 4 5 6 7 8 9 10   23   11 10 09 08 07 06 05

Table of Contents

READING COMPREHENSION

Terrific Trips *(Finding the main idea)* 6

Man vs. Machine *(Sequencing)* 8

Amazing Animals *(Reading for details)* 9

Burger Time *(Using context clues)* 12

The Storm Is Coming *(Identifying cause and effect)* 16

A Timely Business *(Drawing conclusions)* 20

From Pole to Pole *(Identifying fact or opinion)* 23

GRAMMAR

Types of Sentences 28

Compound Sentences 29

Common and Proper Nouns 30

Singular and Plural Nouns 31

Possessive Nouns 32

Verb Tenses 33

Pronouns 34

Adjectives 35

Prepositions 36

Adverbs 37

Commas and Colons 38

WRITING

Body Facts *(Writing sentences)* 40

Clearly Interesting *(Expanding sentences)* 42

A Capital Adventure *(Capitalizing)* 44

And the Winner Is . . . *(Using commas in sentences)* 46

Time to Experiment *(Combining sentences to make compound
   sentences)* 48

Powerful Paragraphs *(Identifying the parts of a paragraph)* 50

CHARTS, TABLES & GRAPHS

Mathematics: Tables 54
Mathematics: Pictographs 56
Mathematics: Bar Graphs 58
Mathematics: Circle Graphs 60
Reading/Language Arts: Charts 62
Reading/Language Arts: Tables 64
Social Studies: Flow Charts 66
Social Studies: Bar Graphs 68
Social Studies: Line Graphs 70
Science: Timeline 72

MATH

Cow Rounding *(Rounding and estimating)* 76
The Next Number. . . *(Number patterns)* 77
A "World" of Averages *(Averaging)* 78
Times Terms *(Reason and logic)* 80
Changing Shapes *(Story problems)* 81
Break the Ice With Perimeter and Area *(Perimeter and area)* 82
A Royal Riddle *(Equivalent measures)* 83
Water Slide Mathematics *(Adding greater numbers)* 84
Fishing for Money *(Adding money)* 86
A Riddle to Grow On *(Subtracting 3- and 4-digit numbers)* 87
Money! Money! Money! *(Subtracting money)* 88
Multiplication Is Cool! *(Reviewing multiplication facts)* 89
Division in Motion *(Reviewing division facts)* 90
Division Fireworks *(Dividing by tens)* 91
Let's Head 'Em Up and Move 'Em Out! *(Dividing with remainders)* . .92
Number Stumper *(Mixed operations)* 94

READING
COMPREHENSION

Terrific Trips

 *The **main idea** tells what a story or paragraph is mostly about.*

Kelly's friends all sent her letters from their trips. Read each letter. Then circle the main idea of each paragraph.

Dear Kelly,

Greetings from New York City! Yesterday we visited Central Park, one of the biggest city parks I have ever seen. It is over one-half mile wide and two and one-half miles long with so much to do. We took a carriage ride through the park and even rowed a boat out on one of the park's lakes. My mom loved looking at all the sculptures in the park. Dad enjoyed the free classical music concert in one of the small pavilions. My brother and I liked the zoo most of all. It was small but had some neat animals. Our guide said the Central Park Zoo is the oldest zoo in the United States.

In the afternoon, we took a ferry to see the famous Statue of Liberty that stands in New York Harbor. Our guide said this 151-foot copper statue was given to the United States by France in 1884 to represent the friendship and freedom both countries share. The tour guide told us that between 1820 and 1937, more than 37 million people came to the United States and were greeted by this statue as they entered our country at Ellis Island. For them it represented the freedom and opportunity they would find in our country. Dad said my own grandparents came to this country through Ellis Island and often spoke of how excited they were to be greeted by "Miss Liberty." Seeing the Statue of Liberty made me so proud of our country and the freedom we have.

Well, I better run. We are going to try to see a Broadway play. See you soon.

Love,
Christie

1. Paragraph 1

   a. Central Park has activities for visitors of all ages and interests.

   b. New York is an incredible city.

   c. The Central Park Zoo is the oldest zoo in the United States.

2. Paragraph 2

   a. The 151-foot Statue of Liberty is impressive.

   b. Immigrants came to this country searching for freedom.

   c. The Statue of Liberty is a symbol of freedom, opportunity, and
      friendship.

Man vs. Machine

Legends are stories that are told as if they are true. They are set in the real world and are often about a real character. However, the character in a legend is often stronger, smarter, bigger, or better than a real person.

The Legend of John Henry

When John Henry was born, the earth shook and lightning struck. He weighed 44 pounds! Shortly after birth, baby John Henry reached for a hammer hanging on the wall. His father knew John Henry was going to be a steel-driving man.

Sure enough, John Henry grew up and worked for the railroad. He was the fastest, strongest steel-driving man in the world. No one could drive more spikes with a hammer than John Henry.

Around 1870, the steam drill was invented. It was said that this machine could dig a hole faster than 20 workers using hammers. A company building a tunnel on one end of a railroad decided to try out the machine. John Henry's company was working on the other end of the tunnel, using men to drill. Both companies bragged and boasted that they were the fastest. Finally, the companies decided to have a race to see which was faster—the steam drill or man. It was John Henry against the steam drill.

Swinging a 20-pound hammer in each hand, John Henry hammered so fast that sparks flew! At the end of the day he had beaten the drill by four feet! That night, John Henry lay down, very proud of his accomplishment, closed his eyes, and never woke up.

Number the events in order.

_____ John Henry hammered so hard that sparks flew.

_____ John Henry was born weighing 44 pounds.

_____ A company decided to try out the new steam drill.

_____ They decided to have a race to see if John Henry could beat the steam drill.

_____ John Henry beat the steam drill and then lay down and died.

_____ John Henry reached for a hammer hanging on a wall.

_____ John Henry grew up and became a steel-driving man.

Amazing Animals

All animals are fascinating, and some are truly amazing! For example, did you know that sharks' teeth are as hard as steel, or that kangaroo rats can survive longer without water than camels? Study the chart below to learn more about several amazing animals.

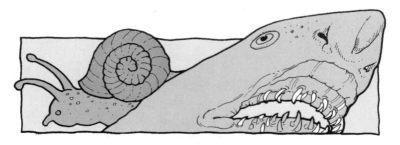

Animal	Where It Lives	Vertebrate or Invertebrate	Fascinating Fact
albatross	near most oceans	vertebrate	can sleep while flying
caterpillar	all over the world	invertebrate	has three times as many muscles as humans
chameleon	forests in Africa and Madagascar	vertebrate	can move its eyes in two different directions at the same time
cockroach	all over the world	invertebrate	can live for up to a week without a head
crocodile	tropical climates	vertebrate	eats only about 50 meals a year
giant squid	oceans throughout the world	invertebrate	has eyes bigger than a human head
giraffe	grasslands in Africa	vertebrate	tallest of animals; has only seven neck bones
penguin	in the southern half of the world with cold ocean waters	vertebrate	eggs kept warm by male until hatched
octopus	oceans throughout the world	invertebrate	has three hearts
shark	oceans throughout the world	vertebrate	never runs out of teeth
snail	almost everywhere—forests, deserts, rivers, ponds, oceans	invertebrate	can sleep for almost three years without waking up
sperm whale	oceans throughout the world	vertebrate	can hold its breath for up to 60 minutes

Use the chart from page 9 to answer the questions below.

1. Which animal(s) live in the ocean? _____

_____

2. What do the giant squid and the chameleon have in common? _____

_____

3. Which animal would delight the "Tooth Fairy"? _____

4. Label the animals that have backbones with a V.

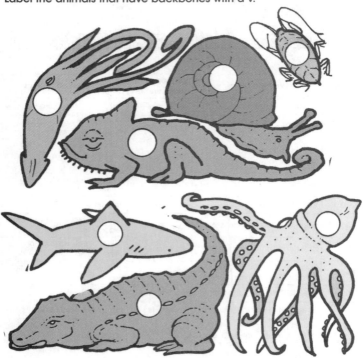

5. Which animals live all, or nearly all, over the world? _____

_____

_____

_____

_____

_____

6. Which animal is very muscular? _____

7. Which animal eats an average of about once a week? _____

8. Which animal can live headless for about a week? _____

9. What is fascinating about a chameleon's eyes? _____

_____

10. Which animal is a "super snoozer"? _____

11. Which animal can hold its breath for nearly an hour? _____

12. Which animal has seven bones in its neck? _____

Burger Time

 Context clues are words or sentences that can help a reader determine the meaning of a new word.

Reese was **famished**! It was nearly two o'clock, and he had not eaten since breakfast. Reese asked his mom if she would stop at a fast food restaurant on their way home from his baseball game. She rolled her eyes and shook her head. His mother absolutely **loathed** fast food, but with over 300,000 fast food restaurants in

the United States, she found it hard to **avoid** them. They were everywhere!

Reese's mother **reluctantly** agreed to **indulge** her son with a fast food lunch, but on the way to the restaurant she tried to explain to Reese the importance of a healthy diet. She had always been a healthy food **fanatic** and knew a lot about foods. She explained to Reese that although fast food is **convenient** to order and very tasty, it often contains **excessive** fat and calories. Reese agreed that a diet of only hamburgers and fries would be unhealthy, and he promised to **definitely** eat a variety of **nutritious** foods as well.

While at the restaurant, Reese's mother began to talk about some of the strange and **unusual** foods eaten by people around the world. In China, for example, some restaurants serve bird's nest soup made from the nests of swallows. Reese was not aware that in Columbia moviegoers may purchase paper cones filled with fried ants as a snack. He was relieved that theaters in the United States served popcorn instead of fried ants. His mother also told him about fugu, a special kind of fish served in Japanese restaurants. If not prepared correctly, fugu can be highly **toxic**. Those who cook it must be specially trained, so the diners do not get sick or die from their meal. Much safer meals included the horse-meat sandwiches served in restaurants in the Netherlands and the grilled guinea pig enjoyed in South American countries. As his mother was explaining how Scottish cooks prepare haggis, a boiled sheep stomach stuffed with oatmeal, Reese began to feel **nauseated** and asked her to please stop talking until he had finished his lunch.

Looking at Reese's pale face, his mother took **pity** on him and promised not to talk about any more strange foods. She did remind him, though, that just because the food was different from what he was used to eating, it was not necessarily bad. In fact, the people in other countries enjoy their food as much as Reese enjoyed fast food. Reese agreed that was probably true, but now all he wanted to enjoy was an ice cream cone for dessert.

Use the story from pages 12-13 to answer the questions below.

1. Use context clues from the story to write each bolded word from the story next to its definition.

a. sick to one's stomach _____

b. to give in to the wishes of _____

c. a devoted person _____

d. sympathy _____

e. more than what is acceptable _____

f. to keep away from _____

g. unwillingly _____

h. easy to reach _____

i. starving _____

j. certainly _____

k. healthy _____

l. disliked intensely _____

m. poisonous _____

2. Reese's mother loathed fast food. Name two foods that you loathe.

_____

_____

3. What does it mean to say a meal is nutritious? _____

_____

_____

4. What are three nutritious foods that you enjoy? _____

_____

_____

5. Fugu may be toxic if it is not prepared correctly. Would you order fugu

in a Japanese restaurant? Why or why not? _____

_____

_____

_____

The Storm Is Coming

*The **cause** is what makes something happen. The **effect** is what happens as a result of the cause.*

Haley was so sad. She just couldn't believe it! She was supposed to have her birthday party tomorrow at Super Kool Skateboard Park, but now there was a chance that the city was going to get hit by a hurricane. The party was canceled and would have to be rescheduled. At least Haley's mom had already

picked up her birthday cake, so now she could have two cakes.

The meteorologist at the weather center had been keeping a very close eye on Hurricane Dora. This fierce storm originated way out in the Atlantic Ocean near Africa. It was now quickly heading towards the southern part of the United States—somewhere near Miami, which is where Haley lived. The storm had winds of up to 120 miles per hour. This made it a category three hurricane, and Haley knew it could be very damaging. Her city had experienced a number of hurricanes.

So instead of running around with her mom doing last-minute things for her party, Haley was busy helping her mom update their hurricane safety kit. They needed new batteries for the flashlights and radios, fresh water, some canned goods, a new can opener, bread, peanut butter, and any other non-perishable food and drink items Haley could talk her mom into buying. Their kit still had plenty of bandages, blankets, and diapers and baby food for her baby brother. Haley's mom asked Haley to also remind her to get some cash while she was at the store.

While Haley and her mom were busy at the store, Haley's dad was busy at the dock securing their boat. When he finished, he was going to return to the house and cover their windows with plywood that he had already cut for just this kind of emergency.

When all of the preparations are done, Haley's parents will gather their files of important papers, some cherished family photos, and a few clothes for everyone. They will pack everything in their van. Since Haley's grandparents live in Atlanta, Haley and her family will evacuate Miami and go stay with them for a few days. Hopefully, they will all be able to return soon. After all, sometimes winds cause hurricanes to change direction, and they miss their intended target completely. Haley hopes this will happen, but she is also excited that she will get to visit her grandparents.

Use the story from pages 16-17 to answer the questions below.

1. Write C for cause or E for effect for each pair of sentences.

_____ Haley's birthday party was canceled.

_____ A hurricane was approaching Haley's city.

_____ The meteorologist was watching Hurricane Dora very closely.

_____ Hurricane Dora was a dangerous, category three hurricane.

_____ Haley's dad was prepared for a hurricane.

_____ Haley's dad had plywood already cut for their windows.

2. Match each cause with its effect.

Cause	Effect
_____ Haley gets to visit her grandparents.	A. Sometimes hurricanes miss their intended target.
_____ Winds change their direction.	B. Haley's family is evacuating.
_____ The storm is very dangerous.	C. Haley is excited.

3. List the items Haley's family have in their hurricane safety kit.

_____

_____

_____

_____

_____

_____

_____

_____

_____

_____

4. What other items might the family need? Why?

_____

_____

_____

_____

_____

A Timely Business

 To **draw conclusions** is to use the information in a story to make a logical assumption.

April 15, 1860—The mail did get through! The pony express mail delivery service is happy to announce that its riders finished the first complete run from Saint Joseph, Missouri, to Sacramento, California. It originated on April 3.

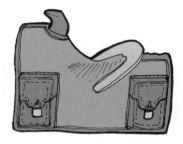

For those of you unfamiliar with the pony express, this impressive service employs men who ride fast ponies or horses, relay-style, across a 1,966-mile trail. These men carry letters and small packages. They promise delivery from one end of the trail to the other in 10 days or less!

Finally, there is a way to communicate long distance with friends and acquaintances. You will not have to rely on slow boats or stagecoaches. About 180 riders, 400 fast horses, and 190 pony express stations make up the pony express. Its riders are generally of small build, and many are teenagers. A day's work consists of about a 75-mile trip, with stops at several stations. The stations are about 10 to 15 miles apart. Riders earn about $100 to $150 a month.

Currently, it costs $5.00 to send half an ounce of mail. However, the price could fall to $1.00 in the future if the service continues to do well. Mail usually travels at a rate of about 200 miles a day.

The pony express operates both day and night to ensure timely delivery of important letters and packages. Its riders work in all kinds of weather and even face attacks by Indians. Be kind if you see a hard-working rider.

October 26, 1861—Sad news for the pony express. After operating for only about 19 months, the service closed its doors today. This came just 2 days after the opening of the transcontinental telegraph, a device that has revolutionized long-distance communication. Needless to say, the pony express faces huge monetary losses.

The closing comes just months after the pony express service boasted of a 7-day, 17-hour delivery from St. Joseph, Missouri, to Sacramento, California. The record-breaking ride delivered a copy of President Abraham Lincoln's first address to Congress.

1. **Underline each statement that could have happened after the pony express closed.**

   People relied on boats and stagecoaches for mail delivery.

   Pony express riders had to find new jobs.

   There were many fast horses for sale.

   News traveled more quickly by means of the transcontinental telegraph.

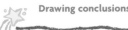

Use the story from pages 20-21 to answer the questions below.

2. How do you think people felt about the pony express closing?

_____

_____

_____

_____

_____

3. Circle how you think the pony express
   riders felt after the pony express closed.

   relieved   sad

   defeated   enlightened

4. Underline what you think would have happened to
   the pony express if it had stayed open after the
   transcontinental telegraph opened.

   The pony express would have hired more riders.

   People would have stopped using the pony
   express once they realized how much more efficient it was to
   communicate over distance by means of the transcontinental
   telegraph.

   The pony express would have built several more trails for their
   riders to use.

From Pole to Pole

*A **fact** is information that can be proven.*
(Example: Antarctica is a continent.)

*An **opinion** is information that tells what someone thinks.*
(Example: The South Pole is the most challenging area to explore.)

Antarctica and the Arctic region are the most southern and northern areas on Earth. These extremely cold areas have been the destinations for many scientific explorations.

Antarctica surrounds the South Pole. It is the coldest of the seven continents. Masses of ice and snow, about one-mile thick, cover most of Antarctica's land. It is the most desolate place on Earth. Few plants can survive in its extreme cold, and its only wildlife lives on the coast.

There is no sunlight at all for months at a time in Antarctica. This keeps the continent very cold. In the winter, temperatures drop below -40°F on the coast and to about -100°F inland. Because it is so cold, little snow falls in this area. The South Pole only gets four-to-six inches of snow each year. However, the existing snow is packed so heavily and tightly that it has formed a great ice cap. This ice cap covers more than 95% of Antarctica.

It is probably not surprising that there are no cities or towns in Antarctica. In fact, no people live there permanently. Since Antarctica was discovered in 1820, many teams of scientists and explorers have braved its cold to learn about this interesting piece of land.

Although very little grows in Antarctica, the seacoast does have a variety of animal life. Whales, seals, penguins, petrels, and fish are among the animals that live in and near Antarctica's coastal waters. All of these animals depend on the sea for food and shelter.

continued...

On the opposite end of Earth is the North Pole. This is also a very cold region. It is called the Arctic. It includes the Arctic Ocean and thousands of islands. The northern parts of Europe, Asia, and North America are also part of this region.

Unlike Antarctica, the Arctic is a permanent home for many people. About 90 percent of all Arctic lands are free of snow and ice in the summer—except for Greenland. Although the sun never shines on much of the Arctic during the winter, it does shine on all parts of this area for at least a little while each day from March to September.

As in Antarctica, little plant life can survive in the Arctic. It is plagued not only by cold, but also by wind, a lack of water, and the long, dark winters. Willow trees do grow in the far north of the Arctic but only a few inches high. A permanently frozen layer of soil, called "permafrost," prevents roots from growing deep enough in the ground to properly anchor plants. Therefore, even if plants could survive the cold, they could not grow roots deep enough to enable them to grow very large.

Because it is warmer than Antarctica, the Arctic is home to such animals as reindeer, caribou, bears, and sables. These animals live in pastures all over the Arctic. The seacoast is also home to many birds, including old squaw ducks, eider ducks, falcons, geese, and loons.

1. Write F for fact or O for opinion.

   ____ Antarctica is the coldest of all the continents.

   ____ People do not live in Antarctica because it is too dark without sunshine every day.

   ____ Farmers would be easily frustrated trying to get things to grow in the Arctic.

   ____ There are no permanent residents in Antarctica.

   ____ Antarctica is the most desolate place on Earth.

   ____ The Arctic includes the northern parts of three continents.

   ____ People who live in the Arctic enjoy Greenland about 90 percent of the time.

   ____ Several kinds of animals live in the Arctic.

2. Why do you think people live in the Arctic but not in Antarctica?

   _____

   _____

   _____

3. Do you think people will one day live in Antarctica?

   _____

   _____

   _____

4. Write *C* for cause or *E* for effect in each pair of sentences.

____ Antarctica is extremely cold.

____ No one lives permanently in Antarctica.

____ "Permafrost" prevents roots from growing very deep in the Arctic

____ There is a permanently frozen layer of soil called "permafrost" in the Arctic.

5. Circle the main idea of the second paragraph.

Antarctica is the coldest place on Earth.

Antarctica is covered with huge amounts of ice and snow.

Antarctica is a very cold place and cannot support much life.

6. Using context clues from the story, write a definition for each word.

desolate _____

permanent _____

plagued _____

GRAMMAR

Types of Sentences

> **RETEACHING:** A **declarative** sentence makes a statement and ends with a period.
> An **interrogative** sentence asks a question and ends with a question mark.
> An **imperative** sentence gives a command and ends with a period or an
> exclamation point. An **exclamatory** sentence shows strong feeling and ends
> with an exclamation mark.

A. Identify each type of sentence by writing *declarative*, *interrogative*,
imperative, or *exclamatory* on the line.

1. Are you ready to write a story? _____

2. I need help! _____

3. Not every story gets printed. _____

4. Tell me a good ending. _____

5. We ate salad and roast beef. _____

6. I couldn't wait for lunch! _____

B. Read each group of words below. If it has a subject and a predicate
and expresses a complete thought, write *complete* on the line.
If it is not a complete sentence, write *incomplete*.

1. With my fork. _____

2. She liked my poem. _____

3. Was proud. _____

4. I'll write another letter. _____

Compound Sentences

A. Circle the conjunction in parentheses ( ) that makes sense.

1. I want to go to the movies, _____ my friend Pat does not. (or, but)

2. It rained last night, _____ we had to stay home. (and, but)

3. Ed will drive to Texas, _____ he will take the train. (or, and)

4. It snowed this morning, _____ the sun came out this afternoon. (but, or)

Common and Proper Nouns

RETEACHING: A **common noun** names any person, place, or thing. A **proper noun**
names a specific person, place, or thing and begins with a capital letter.

A. **Read the following sentences. Circle the proper noun(s) in each sentence and then write what it names on the line. The first one has been done for you.**

1. I read the *Dallas Morning News* every day. _____*newspaper*_____

2. We have two dogs, named Archie and Samantha. _____

3. In the fall, I will attend Nichols Middle School. _____

4. We are going to read about the Industrial Revolution. _____

5. Did you have a good time at our Fourth of July picnic
   this year?_____

6. I want to join the National Geographic Society. ——————————

Singular and Plural Nouns

RETEACHING: A **singular noun** names one person, place, thing, or idea. A **plural noun** names more than one person, place, thing, or idea. A plural noun is most often formed by adding -s to the singular. Some nouns add -es to form the plural.

A. **Read the sentences below. Circle any singular nouns in each sentence and underline any plural common nouns.**

1. He loved walking in the park, taking pictures.

2. He had taken several photographs with his camera when he stopped to rest on a bench.

3. A rabbit scurried through the bushes, and several birds sang in the branches above his head.

4. Then, suddenly, two strangers came down the path and headed toward him.

5. As they ran past, they dropped some notes near his right foot.

6. He picked them up and saw that the paper was in code.

7. "I guess this is another case for the members of our agency," he said.

Possessive Nouns

> **RETEACHING:** A **possessive noun** shows ownership. To form the possessive of a singular noun, add 's. To form the possessive of a plural noun ending in -s, add an apostrophe. To form the possessive of a plural noun that does not end in -s, add 's.

A. Underline the possessive noun in each sentence. On the line following each sentence, write *S* if the possessive noun is singular and *P* if it is plural.

1. Amelia's record flight across the Atlantic occurred in 1932. _____

2. During the Atlantic crossing, ice formed on the plane's wings. _____

3. Mexico's president greeted Amelia when she completed another flight from California to Mexico City. _____

4. Amelia Earhart was always interested in women's roles in aviation. _____

5. Men's career choices in aviation were more numerous at the time. _____

6. A university's financial support helped Amelia realize her dream of attempting a flight around the world. _____

Verb Tenses

The verbs in the following sentences are underlined. Read each sentence. Then write the tense (past, present, future) of each verb on the line.

1. The family <u>arrived</u> in San Francisco. _____

2. The boat <u>stopped</u> there. _____

3. Soon the family <u>will drive</u> across the country. _____

4. They <u>travel</u> for several days. _____

5. The author's father <u>crosses</u> an old bridge. _____

6. The car practically <u>raced</u> across the bridge. _____

7. This action <u>scared</u> both mother and daughter. _____

8. They <u>will remember</u> it forever! _____

9. They <u>will hope</u> for no more similar events. _____

10. The family <u>settled</u> in an overnight cabin. _____

Pronouns

> **RETEACHING:** A **pronoun** is a word that takes the place of a noun or nouns. Pronouns show number. They indicate one or more than one.

A. **Underline the pronoun in each sentence. Then circle the word or words to which the pronoun refers.**

1. Savannah and Elana agreed to eat lunch together. They decided to meet at noon.

2. "Which train should I take?" David wondered, studying the train schedule.

3. Melanie opened the door. She was surprised when people shouted, "Happy birthday!"

4. The barn might look deserted, but it has become a home to many birds.

5. Frank has already eaten half of the bread he baked this afternoon.

Adjectives

> **RETEACHING:** An **adjective** is a word that tells more about a person, place, or thing. The adjectives *a*, *an*, and *the* are articles.

A. Complete the following phrases. For 1–4, write an adjective.
   For 5–8, write the article *a* or *an* and a noun.

1. a _____ game

2. a _____ street

3. an _____ book

4. an _____ dog

5. _____ incredible _____

6. _____ beautiful _____

7. _____ exciting _____

8. _____ colorful _____

Prepositions

> **RETEACHING: Prepositions** show the relationship between a noun or pronoun and another word or group of words in a sentence such as *in*, *on*, *of*, *for*, or *at*. Groups of words introduced by a preposition are called **prepositional phrases**.

A. **In each sentence, circle the prepositional phrase and underline the preposition.**

1. Gerard is giving a party for Maria.

2. Norma sent invitations to all their friends.

3. The food was made by Josue.

4. Rebecca decorated the room with streamers.

5. Mela sat next to Danielle.

6. Kama played a song on her guitar.

7. Terry arrived late with Deborah.

8. Adriane brought a huge chocolate cake from the bakery.

9. The celebration lasted until dinnertime.

10. Sarah and Joanna took the train home with Liza.

Adverbs

> **RETEACHING:** An **adverb** is a word that describes a verb, an adjective, or another adverb. Some adverbs tell when or where something happens.

A. In each sentence, underline the adverb and circle the verb it describes.

1. Anna jumped quickly into the pool.

2. Danny sat quietly on the sidelines.

3. The dog gently pushed open the door.

4. The animal waited patiently to be fed.

5. Laurie tenderly petted the puppy.

6. The crowd cheered loudly when the team scored a goal.

7. Joseph told him later about the party.

8. Lucy immediately volunteered to make invitations.

9. The cat boldly climbed the tree.

Commas and Colons

RETEACHING: Commas are used to separate items in a series, to separate parts of dates, to separate parts of names when the last name is written first, and to follow the greeting and closing of letters. **Colons** are used to separate hours and minutes in expressions of time, to introduce a list, and to follow the greeting of a business letter.

A. Read each sentence. Add a comma or colon where needed. Write *correct* if the sentence is correct.

1. Luke Sam and Nick are putting on a play.

2. The play will begin at 800 PM.

3. Yalixa his sister wrote the play.

4. They will perform the play Wednesday and Thursday.

5. Amy can you make the costumes?

6. Like her mom Luisa is a good singer.

7. Our flag is red white and blue.

8. Michael plays baseball and soccer.

9. Nathan will visit on March 28 2004.

10. We are always happy when he comes but sad when he leaves.

WRITING

Body Facts

A **sentence** *is a group of words that expresses a complete thought.*
There are four kinds of sentences.

A **declarative sentence** *is a* **statement**. *It gives information and ends with a period.*

I just finished a really cool article about the body.

An **interrogative sentence** *is a* **question**. *It asks for information and often begins with who, what, where, when, why, or how. A question ends with a question mark.*

What is the title of the article?

An **imperative sentence** *is a* **command**. *It tells or asks someone to do something. A command usually ends with a period but can also end with an exclamation point.*

Tell me where you read it. Hurry up and tell me!

An **exclamatory sentence** *is an* **exclamation**.
It shows strong feeling or emotion and ends with an exclamation point.

I can't wait to read it now!

Use any or all of the words in each group to write four kinds of sentences. One sentence has been completed for you. Begin and end each sentence correctly.

| do how you many times breathe minute |
| is per that count twenty humans fast |

Interrogative: How many times per minute do humans breathe?

Declarative: _____

_____

Imperative: _____

_____

Exclamatory: _____

_____

sixty-five	believe	the	is	body	water
about	percent	I	it	don't	really

Interrogative: _____

_____

Declarative: _____

_____

Imperative: _____

_____

Exclamatory: _____

_____

how	did	read	small	twenty-two	long	you
	are	the	feet	about	intestines	

Interrogative: _____

_____

Declarative: _____

_____

Imperative: _____

_____

Exclamatory: _____

_____

Clearly Interesting

A sentence may be very simple, but you can make it more interesting by adding adverbs, adjectives, and prepositional phrases. When you add to a sentence, you expand it.

The kitten ran.

adjectives   **adverb**   **prepositional phrase**

The frightened, little kitten ran quickly under the bed.

Add to each list of adjectives, adverbs, and prepositional phrases that has been started.

Adjectives	Adverbs	Prepositional Phrases	
lonely	calmly	over the bridge	with my friends
old	eagerly	through the woods	until noon
friendly	continuously	across the lake	of commuters
beautiful	frequently	out of the building	toward the moon
cranky	yesterday	during rush hour	into the water

_____   _____   _____

_____   _____   _____

_____   _____   _____

_____   _____   _____

_____   _____   _____

_____   _____   _____

_____   _____   _____

Use some of the words and phrases to expand each sentence.

1. **The baby cried.** _____

_____

_____

2. **Thousands left.** _____

_____

_____

3. **The man walked.** _____

_____

_____

4. **The students sat.** _____

_____

_____

5. **I went.** _____

_____

_____

_____

A Capital Adventure

 You know that the first word of a sentence is always capitalized. Here are other rules to remember when you write.

Capitalize

• *the names of people and pets.*

My friend, Maggie Ames, has two cats, Hero and Spike.

• *titles of respect such as Dr., Mrs., Mr., Miss, and Ms.*

Mr. Ames and Maggie took the cats to Dr. Jones, the vet, last week.

• *the names of days, months, and holidays, but not the seasons.*

Maggie got Spike on the Tuesday before Thanksgiving last fall.

• *titles of relatives when they are used as a name.*

I can't have a cat because Mom and my sister have allergies.

• *names of places, buildings, and monuments.*

I am taking care of the cats while Maggie and her family are on vacation in New York City.

She is going to visit the Empire State Building and the Statue of Liberty.

• *direction words when they name a region.*

We live in the Southeast. Maggie and her family flew north yesterday morning.

Find and correct 16 errors in capitalization in the paragraph below. Some words should be capitalized and some should not. Mark three lines under each letter that needs to be capitalized (i). Draw a line through each letter that should not be capitalized (Ƀ).

The best time to visit Washington, D.c., is in the early Spring. the weather is just right in april, not too hot or cold. The cherry blossoms were in bloom while we were there, so that made my Mom happy! We got to the Capital early monday morning after a ten-hour drive from the midwest. After checking into our hotel, we decided to visit the national Air and space Museum first. I could have spent all week there, although the Washington monument, the Lincoln Memorial, and the White house were really cool. I was hoping to see the president, but he was in europe. We did see a Senator from our State, though.

And the Winner Is . . .

 As a writer, you need to know how to use commas to let readers know where to pause when reading a sentence.

Use a comma:

- *after each item in a series of three or more, except after the last item.*

  Max wrote, read, and revised his story.

- *to set off the name of the person you are addressing directly.*
  Will you read it one more time, Jamie?

- *after introductory words like yes, no, and well.*
  Yes, I have some time right now.

- *to set off an appositive from the rest of the sentence.*
  The Pen to Paper Club, a writers' organization, sponsored a contest.

- *before a conjunction that joins two sentences.*
  Max entered his story, but he never thought he'd win.

- *after a dependent clause that begins a sentence.*
  When the letter came, Max was too nervous to open it.

- *to set off words that interrupt the basic idea of a sentence.*
  Max's sister, therefore, opened it for him.

- *to separate geographical names and dates.*
  Max won a trip to Orlando, Florida. They left Monday, June 23, 2003.

Write a sentence to answer each question. Include commas where they are needed.

1. On what day and date will you celebrate your next birthday?

_____

2. If you could choose to live in any city or town in any state, where would it be?

_____

3. How would you complete the following sentence?

Whenever I _____

_____

_____

4. Imagine that you have been asked to introduce the President of the United States at a town hall meeting. How would you begin your introduction using direct address?

_____

_____

5. How would you use *and* in a sentence that tells what you had for lunch yesterday and what you had for lunch today?

_____

_____

Time to Experiment

 Combining sentences helps to eliminate the problem of short or choppy sentences in paragraphs. You can often combine related sentences into compound sentences by using the conjunctions and, but, or, *and* so. *Compare the following two paragraphs and decide which is easier to understand.*

Young Alva was curious about everything. That curiosity led him to continually ask questions. His mother had been a teacher. She didn't always know the answers. If no one could tell him, he experimented. Once he wanted to know how hens hatch chickens. He put some eggs in a basket and sat on them. Can you guess who Alva is? Do you need another hint?

Young Alva was curious about everything, and that curiosity led him to continually ask questions. His mother had been a teacher, but she didn't always know the answers. If no one could tell him, he experimented. Once he wanted to know how hens hatch chickens, so he put some eggs in a basket and sat on them. Can you guess who Alva is, or do you need another hint?

Read the paragraph. Place parentheses around the pairs of sentences that can be combined with *and, but, or,* or *so.*

My brother Alex has more "interests" than anyone I know. The novelty always wears off very quickly. I know my brother! Last week, Alex wanted to join the school band. He asked if he could rent a drum set. I burst out laughing. My parents just looked at each other. I knew what they were thinking. Would they be able to convince Alex to try something a little quieter? Would he insist on the drums? Well, they convinced Alex to try something else. It wasn't something quieter. Today he informed us that he's decided to try the tuba. In fact, the school has an extra tuba. Mom and Dad won't have to rent one. Needless to say, I hope this novelty wears off very, very, very quickly!

Powerful Paragraphs

 A **paragraph** is a group of sentences that focuses on a topic and one main idea about that topic. A **topic sentence** expresses that main idea. It may answer who, what, where, when, why, how, or a combination of questions. Although a topic sentence often begins a paragraph, it can come at the end or even in the middle of a paragraph. The other sentences in the paragraph develop the main idea by telling more about it. They are called **supporting sentences**.

Read each paragraph. Underline the topic sentence in each one. Put parentheses around each supporting sentence.

1. There is an energizing chill in the air now that the days are shorter. The last of the crops are about to be harvested, and a blanket of leaves covers much of the landscape. All but a few of our summertime visitors have already flown south for warmer places. Once again, the long, hot days of summer have given way to fall.

2. Falling asleep was never a problem for me until we moved to the country. I was used to the sounds of subway trains pulling into the station near our apartment, the horns and squealing brakes of buses, taxis, and cars, wailing sirens, and planes landing or taking off. I was not used to the sound of chirping crickets. My parents assured me that I would get used to it. They were right, of course, but it took awhile.

3. This amazing marsupial spends about 22 hours a day asleep in a eucalyptus tree. A nocturnal creature, it is mostly active at night. The habits of the world's sleepiest animal, the koala, really fascinate me. When it is awake, the koala feeds on eucalyptus leaves and shoots, up to two pounds at a time. What's more, it seldom drinks water because it gets most of what it needs from the leaves and shoots.

CHARTS, TABLES
& GRAPHS

Going for the Gold

Every two years, countries from around the world compete in either the Summer or the Winter Olympics. This table shows the number of medals won by different countries at the 2000 Summer Olympic Games in Sydney, Australia. Use the table to choose the best answer to each question.

SUMMER OLYMPIC GAMES, 2000: MEDAL COUNT				
Nation	**Gold**	**Silver**	**Bronze**	**Total**
United States	39	25	33	97
Russia	32	28	28	88
China	28	16	15	59
Australia	16	25	17	58
Germany	14	17	26	57
France	13	14	11	38
Italy	13	8	13	34
Cuba	11	11	7	29
Britain	11	10	7	28
South Korea	8	9	11	28
Romania	11	6	9	26
Netherlands	12	9	4	25

1 How many medals did China win in all?

ⓐ 28 ⓑ 57 ⓒ 59 ⓓ 88

2 Which country won the greatest number of silver medals?

ⓐ United States ⓑ Russia ⓒ Germany ⓓ Australia

3 How many gold medals did the United States win?

ⓐ 97 ⓑ 88 ⓒ 58 ⓓ 39

4 How many medals did Cuba win in all?

ⓐ 29 ⓑ 28 ⓒ 11 ⓓ 7

5 Which of these countries won the fewest gold medals?

ⓐ Britain ⓑ Netherlands ⓒ Romania ⓓ South Korea

6 Australia won how many more medals than France?

ⓐ 1 ⓑ 19 ⓒ 20 ⓓ 24

Sailing the Seas

Merchant ships set sail from ports in countries around the world.
The pictograph below displays the number of ships sailing from six of these
countries. Use the graph to choose the best answer to each question.

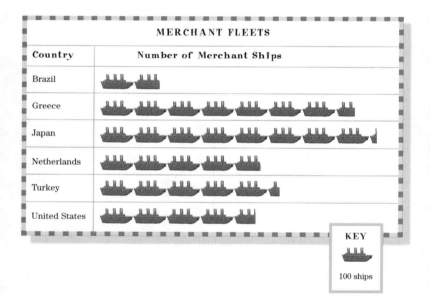

MERCHANT FLEETS	
Country	Number of Merchant Ships
Brazil	🚢🚢
Greece	🚢🚢🚢🚢🚢🚢🚢
Japan	🚢🚢🚢🚢🚢🚢🚢
Netherlands	🚢🚢🚢🚢
Turkey	🚢🚢🚢🚢🚢
United States	🚢🚢🚢🚢🚢

KEY

🚢

100 ships

1 About how many ships sail from Greece?

  ⓐ 7   ⓒ 77

  ⓑ 8   ⓓ 770

2 Which of these countries has the most ships?

  ⓐ Brazil   ⓒ Japan

  ⓑ Greece   ⓓ Turkey

3 Compared with the Netherlands' fleet, about how many more ships does Japan have?

  ⓐ 330   ⓒ 33

  ⓑ 320   ⓓ 32

4 Which country has a fleet of about 475 ships?

  ⓐ Greece   ⓒ Turkey

  ⓑ Japan   ⓓ United States

5 Russia's merchant fleet has 1513 ships. How many ship symbols would be used to represent Russia's fleet on this graph?

  ⓐ 1.513   ⓒ 151.3

  ⓑ 15.13   ⓓ 1513

6 Which ratio best represents the size of Brazil's fleet compared with Turkey's fleet?

  ⓐ 1:2   ⓒ 2:1

  ⓑ 1:3   ⓓ 3:1

Popular Parks

Millions of people visited national parks in the year 2000. The bar graph below shows the numbers of visitors to six of the most popular parks. Use the graph to answer the questions.

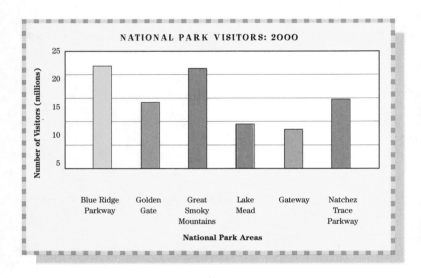

1 Which national park area had the most visitors in 2000?

_____

2 Which of these six areas had the fewest visitors in 2000?

_____

3 About how many people visited the Great Smoky Mountains National Park in 2000?

_____

4 Which area had just about the same number of visitors as the Golden Gate?

_____

5 About how many more people visited the Golden Gate than Lake Mead?

_____

Great Game Graph!

How much time do kids really spend playing video games? Read the circle graph to find out.

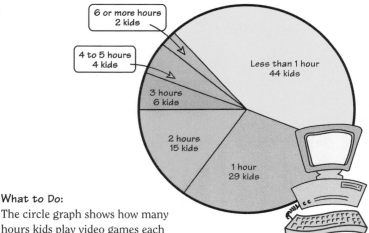

How Long Kids Play Video Games Each Day

6 or more hours
2 kids

4 to 5 hours
4 kids

Less than 1 hour
44 kids

3 hours
6 kids

2 hours
15 kids

1 hour
29 kids

What to Do:
The circle graph shows how many hours kids play video games each day. The number of kids shown in each section is out of 100 kids. For example, look at the bottom section. It shows that out of every 100 kids, 29 play video games for 1 hour a day. Use the graph to answer the questions.

1. How many kids out of 100 play video games for 2 hours a day? _____

2. How many hours a day do 6 out of 100 kids play video games? _____

3. For how long does the largest group of kids play video games each day? _____

4. For how long does the smallest group of kids play video games each day? _____

5. Do more or less than $\frac{1}{2}$ of the kids play video games for less than 1 hour

   a day? _____

6. Think of the amount of time you play video games each day. What is the
   section of the graph where you would be? _____

Mythology Trivia

Summer Olympic Games from 1968 through 2000. Use the graph to answer the questions.

GODS AND GODDESSES		
Roman Names	**Duties**	**Greek Names**
Jupiter	Lord of the sky and ruler of all the gods	Zeus
Juno	Wife of Jupiter/Zeus and protector of marriage	Hera
Mars	God of war	Ares
Minerva	Goddess of wisdom, arts, and battle	Athena
Neptune	Ruler of the seas	Poseidon
Pluto	Ruler of the underworld and wealth	Hades
Diana	Goddess of hunting and youth	Artemis
Venus	Goddess of love and beauty	Aphrodite
Mercury	Messenger of the gods	Hermes

1. For the Romans, who was the leader of all the gods?

_____

2. What was Minerva's function?

_____

3. In ancient Greece, who was the ruler of the underworld?

_____

4. For the Greeks, who was the goddess of love?

_____

5. Who was the messenger of the gods in these two different cultures?

_____

6. What was Diana's duty in ancient Rome?

_____

Canadian Travels

Imagine you are taking a trip to Nova Scotia, Canada. Use this table of contents from a travel guide to choose the best answer to each question.

CONTENTS

How to Get to Nova Scotia 3

Visitor Services 9

Calendar of Festivals and Events 15

Attractions 21

Bay of Fundy 25

Cape Breton Island 31

Halifax 47

Kejimkujik National Park 59

Northumberland Strait 71

Campgrounds 93

Lodging and Restaurants 105

Points of Interest 193

History 207

Maps 215

Travel Tips 219

Recreation 225

Customs Information 239

Index 241

1. On which pages would you find information about things to see in Halifax?

   ⓐ pages 15–20   ⓑ pages 21–24   ⓒ pages 47–58   ⓓ pages 71–92

2. Which section of the book probably has information about early settlers in Nova Scotia?

   ⓐ How to Get to Nova Scotia   ⓑ Visitor Services

   ⓒ Customs Information   ⓓ History

3. To find information about hotels, you should begin reading on what page?

   ⓐ page 9   ⓑ page 105   ⓒ page 219   ⓓ page 22

4. To find information about fishing and hiking, you should look under —

   ⓐ Recreation   ⓑ Travel Tips   ⓒ Campgrounds   ⓓ Maps

5. On which pages should you look for a schedule of special events that take place in August?

   ⓐ pages 15–20   ⓑ pages 25–30   ⓒ pages 193–206 ⓓ pages 219–224

The Story of Cotton

Ms. William's 5th grade class is studying how cotton becomes fabric. Use the flow chart to answer the questions.

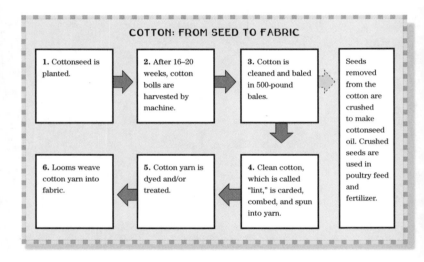

COTTON: FROM SEED TO FABRIC

1. Cottonseed is planted.

2. After 16–20 weeks, cotton bolls are harvested by machine.

3. Cotton is cleaned and baled in 500-pound bales.

Seeds removed from the cotton are crushed to make cottonseed oil. Crushed seeds are used in poultry feed and fertilizer.

6. Looms weave cotton yarn into fabric.

5. Cotton yarn is dyed and/or treated.

4. Clean cotton, which is called "lint," is carded, combed, and spun into yarn.

1. How long do cotton plants grow before the bolls are harvested?

_____

2. What is the third step in the process of making cotton fabric?

_____

3. According to this flow chart, what is lint?

_____

4. What happens to the cotton just after it is spun into yarn?

_____

5. What kind of machine is used to weave cotton yarn into fabric?

_____

6. Name four products made from cotton plants.

_____

Vacation Hot Spots

Where would you like to go on your next vacation? This bar graph shows the number of visitors to the top six tourist destinations in the world in 1999. Use the graph to choose the best answer to each question.

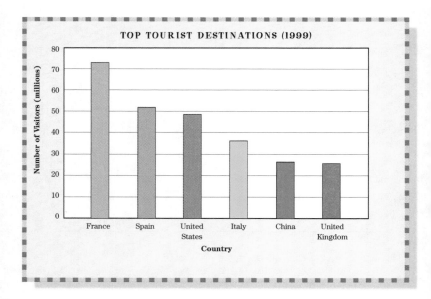

1 Which country had the most visitors?

   ⓐ Spain   ⓑ United States ⓒ France   ⓓ United Kingdom

2 About how many people visited Italy?

   ⓐ 27 million   ⓑ 36 million   ⓒ 48 million   ⓓ 52 million

3 Spain had about how many more visitors than China?

   ⓐ 2 million   ⓑ 5 million   ⓒ 15 million   ⓓ 25 million

4 Which country had the fewest visitors?

   ⓐ United Kingdom ⓑ France   ⓒ Italy   ⓓ China

5 Which statement about the information on this graph is correct?

   ⓐ The United States is the top tourist destination.

   ⓑ Four of the top six destinations are in Europe.

   ⓒ All the most popular destinations are in Asia.

   ⓓ More people visit China than any other country.

Rose's Baby-sitting Business

Last year, Rose had several baby-sitting jobs. The line graph below shows how much money she earned each month. Use the graph to choose the best answer to each question.

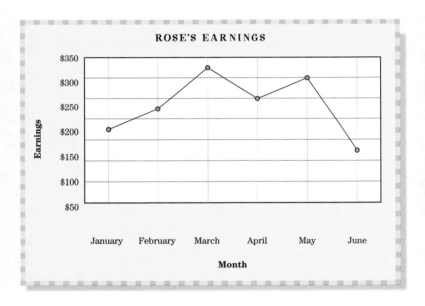

1. In which month did Rose earn the most money?

    ⓐ January   ⓒ May

    ⓑ March   ⓓ June

2. About how much did Rose earn in February?

    ⓐ $225   ⓒ $275

    ⓑ $250   ⓓ $325

3. About how much more did Rose earn in April than in January?

    ⓐ $25   ⓒ $75

    ⓑ $50   ⓓ $100

4. In which month did Rose earn the least?

    ⓐ January   ⓒ April

    ⓑ February   ⓓ June

5. About how much did Rose earn in the six months combined?

    ⓐ $1000   ⓒ $1600

    ⓑ $1400   ⓓ $2000

Technology Trivia

Throughout history, inventions and discoveries in technology have pushed civilization in new directions. Use the timeline below to answer the questions about some of these technological advances.

ADVANCES IN TECHNOLOGY: 1700–1900

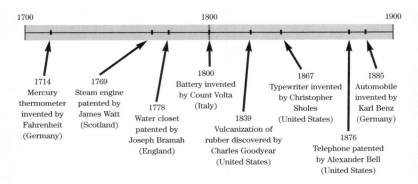

☐ What invention was patented in 1769?

_____

☐ In what country was the water closet invented?

_____

☐ Who invented the battery, and in what year?

_____

☐ What did Charles Goodyear discover in 1839?

_____

_____

_____

☐ According to the timeline, what two inventions were made in Germany?

_____

_____

_____

☐ When was the typewriter invented, and by whom?

_____

_____

MATH

Cow Rounding

Riddle: What do cows give after an earthquake?

Round each number. Then use the Decoder to solve the riddle by filling in the spaces at the bottom of the page.

Decoder

700	F
11,000	K
800	S
2,780	O
3,600	U
1,000	M
9,900	Y
24,400	I
73,000	S
5,000	L
24,000	P
6,000	Q
2,770	E
7,500	T
9,940	A
3,700	K
10,000	R
8,000	H
2,000	N

1. Round 789 to the nearest hundred _____

2. Round 5,112 to the nearest thousand _____

3. Round 3,660 to the nearest hundred _____

4. Round 1,499 to the nearest thousand _____

5. Round 2,771 to the nearest ten _____

6. Round 7,529 to the nearest thousand _____

7. Round 24,397 to the nearest hundred _____

8. Round 10,708 to the nearest thousand _____

9. Round 9,937 to the nearest ten _____

10. Round 73,489 to the nearest thousand _____

__	__	__	__		__	__	__	__	__
4	7	2	8		10	6	9	3	5	1

The Next Number . . .

Sometimes sets of numbers have something in common. They follow a pattern. Take a look at the numbers 4, 6, 8, and 10. As the pattern continues, each number gets larger by 2. Try completing the number patterns in the problems below. Some are tougher to figure out than others. Give 'em a try. Good luck! Use the space below and to the right to work out the problems.

1. 8, 11, 14, 17, 20, _____, _____, _____

2. 27, 29, 31, 33, 35, _____, _____, _____

3. 2, 7, 12, 17, 22, 27, _____, _____, _____

4. 5, 9, 14, 23, 37, 60, _____, _____, _____

5. 39, 46, 53, 60, 67, 74, _____, _____, _____

6. 6, 7, 13, 20, 33, 55, _____, _____

7. 4, 15, 26, 37, 48, _____, _____, _____

8. 93, 116, 209, 325, 534, 859, _____, _____

A "World" of Averages

For many people, Florida's Walt Disney World is a magical place. You might say there's nothing average about it. But if you look closely, you can find lots of averages there!

What's an average? It's a number that describes a group of numbers. It isn't the biggest number in the group, or the smallest. It's somewhere in between. For example, the average number of people that visit Walt Disney World each day is about 77,000.

That doesn't mean that exactly 77,000 people visit the park every day. On a sunny day or a holiday, more than 77,000 people might visit the park. On a rainy day, fewer than 77,000 people might visit. But 77,000—the average—is about how many people visit on most days.

Want to find out more about an average day at Walt Disney World? Read on!

Finding an Average

Say you went on a three-day trip to Walt Disney World. How could you find the average number of hours you walked each day? Here's one way:

Add up the actual number of hours you walked each day:

10 hours + 8 hours + 6 hours = 24 hours

Then divide the total by the number of days you added up.

24 hours ÷ 3 days = 8 hours

You walked an average of 8 hours each day.

> To find the average of any set of numbers, add all the numbers. Then divide the total by the number of numbers in the set. Example: to find the average of 40, 30, 22, and 20, first add. Then divide the total, 112, by 4. The average is 28.

What to Do:

By finding the average of each set of numbers below, learn more about what happens on an "average" day at Walt Disney World.

1. 25 and 175

   About _____ pairs of sunglasses are turned in to the Lost and Found in the Magic Kingdom every day.

2. 5,000 and 7,000

   You can choose from about _____ different food items.

3. 881; 924; and 1,234

   About _____ Mickey Mouse ears are sold.

4. 1,489; 1,584; and 1,640

   The monorail trains travel about _____ miles in and out of the parks.

5. 3,259; 4,039; and 5,443

   About _____ T-shirts are bought.

6. 10,660; 28,069; 58,392; and 78,223

   About _____ packets of ketchup are handed out.

7. 5,400; 10,000; 11,608; and 33,124

   About _____ hamburgers are sold.

8. 117; 3,274; 15,673; and 41,208

   About _____ pounds of potatoes are used to make french fries.

9. 35; 126; 780; 1,050; and 3,009

   About _____ Band-Aids are given out.

Times Terms

Write the multiplication word that fits each clue in the box. When you finish, copy the letters in the shaded boxes. Unscramble these letters to form another multiplication word.

1. Any number multiplied by this number comes out 0. ☐☐☐☐

2. Another word for *multiplied by* is ____. ☐☐☐☐☐

3. This is one of the numbers you multiply. ☐☐☐☐☐☐

4. Multiply a number by 3, and you ____ that number. ☐☐☐☐☐☐

5. Multiply a number by 2 to get the same answer as adding a ____.

☐☐☐☐☐☐

6. The answer when you multiply is called the ____.

☐☐☐☐☐☐☐

7. Its math symbol is x. ☐☐☐☐☐☐☐☐

8. Multiplication is the same as repeated ____. ☐☐☐☐☐☐☐☐☐

9. You can multiply if you have groups that are the ____ ____ (2 words).

☐☐☐☐ ☐☐☐☐☐

Write the letters from the shaded boxes here.

☐☐☐☐☐☐☐☐

Now unscramble them to make another word.

☐☐☐☐☐☐☐☐☐

Changing Shapes

Riddle: How did the square become a triangle?

To find the answer to the riddle, solve the multiplication problems here. (Don't forget units.) Then, match each product with a letter in the Key below. Write the correct letters on the blanks below.

1. Joe has 2 apples. Tim has 2 times as many apples as Joe has. How many apples does Tim have? _____

2. Kendra has 3 books. Paula has 3 times as many books as Kendra has. How many books does Paula have? _____

3. Cliff has 5 times as many baseball caps as Wayne has. Wayne has 5 baseball caps. How many baseball caps does Cliff have? _____

4. Jorge has 10 oranges. Wendy has 2 times as many oranges as Jorge has. How many oranges does Wendy have? _____

5. Martha has 6 times as many coats as Russell has. Russell has 5 coats. How many coats does Martha have? _____

6. Debbie has 9 pairs of shoes. How many shoes does she have in all? _____

7. Michael has 8 bunches of bananas. Each bunch has 7 bananas. How many bananas does he have in all? _____

8. Leroy has 11 times as many pencils as Renee has. Renee has 11 pencils. How many pencils does Leroy have? _____

9. Steve has 6 video games. Jack has 8 times as many video games as Steve has. How many video games do Steve and Jack have in all? _____

10. Carla has 7 chairs. Kim has 7 times as many chairs as Carla has. How many more chairs does Kim have than Carla? _____

Key

4 apples ...... T
20 oranges ... C
18 shoes ..... N
56 bananas ... C
111 pencils I
54 video games E
48 video games F
30 coats ..... U
2 apples ..... S
42 chairs ..... A
15 bananas ... K
9 books ...... R
25 caps ...... R
121 pencils .... O
40 coats ..... B

Riddle Answer: **IT** __ __ __ __ __ __ __ __ __ __ .

Break the Ice With Perimeter and Area

Jessie is building ice skating rinks for her friends. She measures the size of each rink in two ways—**perimeter** and **area**. Perimeter tells the measurement **around** the rink. Area tells how many square units fit **inside** each rink. Some rinks have the same area but different perimeters. Try some building yourself!

You Need:
square crackers or square counters

Here's the rink Jesse built for Shawn. Its area is 4.
Its perimeter is 8.

What to Do:
Use the square crackers to help you answer the questions. Then draw how the crackers look.

1. Shawn wants a bigger rink. He wants it to have a perimeter of 12 and an area of 8. What can you add to Shawn's rink? Draw what it will look like.

2. Gil also wants a rink with a perimeter of 12. But he wants it to be square. What will it look like? What will its area be? Draw what it will look like.

3. The area of Rita's rink is 12. Its perimeter is 14. What does her rink look like? Draw it.

4. Sonia wants her rink to have an area of 16. She says it can be shaped like a square or a rectangle. What could the rink look like? What will its perimeter be? Draw it.

5. José wants a rink with an area of 24. It can be any shape. What are some of the shapes it could be? What are their perimeters? Draw one example.

A Royal Riddle

Riddle: Where does a king stay when he goes to the beach?

To find the answer to the riddle, solve the multiplication problems. Then, match each product with a letter in the Key below. Write the correct letters on the blanks below.

1 How many minutes are there in 1 hour? _____

2 How many minutes are there in 2 hours? _____

3 How many minutes are there in 4 hours? _____

4 How many minutes are there in 5 hours? _____

5 How many minutes are there in 7 hours? _____

6 How many minutes are there in 10 hours? _____

7 How many minutes are there in 11 hours? _____

8 How many minutes are there in 15 hours? _____

9 How many minutes are there in 18 hours? _____

10 How many minutes are there in 20 hours? _____

Key

600	S
420	C
1,200	N
660	S
1,080	T
1,240	M
120	D
180	X
300	A
60	L
900	E
450	B
1,100	I
240	A
360	O

Riddle Answer:

A __ __ __ __   __ __ __ __ __ __

Water Slide Mathematics

Add.

A.

3,412	4,629	3,894	4,168
+2,839	+1,381	+2,009	+2,387

B.

3,986	7,321	4,893	8,142
+2,018	+1,845	+3,125	+3,246

C.

8,465	5,842	4,062	8,132
+3,143	+1,938	+2,389	+1,826

D. 2,035   3,614   4,064   5,429
   +1,846   +2,815   +2,813   +3,846

E. 6,426   5,421   4,684   6,425
   +2,181   +1,846   +2,193   +1,899

F. 8,142   9,242   5,811   2,465
   +1,846   +1,346   +2,398   +1,384

Fishing for Money

  When adding money, keep the decimal point between the hundreds and tens place lined up.

$84.29	$$\begin{array}{c} 1 \ \ 1 \\ \$84.29 \end{array}$$	$84.29
+ 29.16	+ 29.16	+ 29.16
.	113.45	$113.45
Place the decimal point in the sum.	*Add. Regroup as needed.*	*Place the dollar sign in the sum.*

Add.

$3.42	$6.49	$2.47	$9.25	$3.04
+0.29	+9.28	+9.28	+3.98	+2.99

$0.42	$5.48	$6.43	$1.42	$1.99
+8.91	+1.39	+2.97	+3.58	+8.33

$0.03	$0.04	$1.46	$9.42	$31.42
+4.08	3.12	0.82	2.58	+28.29
	+0.98	+3.48	+1.07	

A Riddle to Grow On

Riddle:
What tables
grow on farms?

Do each subtraction problem. Then use the
Decoder to solve the riddle by filling in the
spaces at the bottom of the page.

Decoder

4,884	**T**
64	**C**
275	**D**
459	**V**
286	**W**
1,451	**B**
257	**L**
1,541	**K**
428	**G**
81	**M**
743	**E**
48	**E**
792	**P**
2,869	**S**
12	**Z**
300	**E**
2,942	**Y**
7,926	**A**
7,431	**Q**

❶ $714 - 457 =$ _____

❷ $936 - 508 =$ _____

❸ $1,000 - 700 =$ _____

❹ $1,362 - 619 =$ _____

❺ $2,000 - 549 =$ _____

❻ $3,873 - 1,004 =$ _____

❼ $1,446 - 987 =$ _____

❽ $5,011 - 4,963 =$ _____

❾ $8,600 - 3,716 =$ _____

❿ $9,925 - 1,999 =$ _____

"__ __ __ __" __ __ __ __ __ __
 7 4 2 8   9 10 5 1 3 6

Money! Money! Money!

 When subtracting money, follow these steps.

$100.00
− 89.24
    .

Line up the decimal
points. Place a decimal
point in the difference.

        0 9 9 9
$ ̶1 ̶0̶ ̶0̶ . ̶1̶0̶ ̶1̶0̶
−   8 9 . 2 4
        .

Subtract.

        0 9 9 9
$ ̶1 ̶0̶ ̶0̶ . ̶1̶0̶ ̶1̶0̶
−   8 9 . 2 4

$ 1 0 . 7 6

Place a dollar
sign in the
difference.

Choose an amount from the Money Bank to solve each problem.
Use each amount only once. Be careful! All problems must be solved. Hint:
Start with the greatest numbers first.

A. **$1.00**	B. **$15.00**	C. **$10.00**	D. **$20.00**	E. **$50.00**
−	−	−	−	−

F. **$100.00**	G. **$25.00**	H. **$16.00**	I. **$69.00**	J. **$37.00**
−	−	−	−	−

K. **$44.00**	L. **$80.00**	M. **$4.00**	N. **$40.00**	O. **$11.00**
−	−	−	−	−

Money Bank

$.29	$4.35	$21.45	$9.42	$2.59
$29.92	$7.78	$46.45	$43.49	$17.98
$39.42	$89.49	$12.98	$58.99	$75.49

Multiplication Is Cool!

Multiply. Then use the code to answer the question below.

S. 11 x 12 =	! 11 x 11 =	U. 6 x 9 =
E. 9 x 9 =	K. 8 x 8 =	R. 7 x 7 =
D. 9 x 5 =	T. 3 x 11 =	G. 7 X 9 =
O. 5 x 7 =	A. 8 x 9 =	W. 8 x 4 =
H. 6 x 6 =	N. 10 x 11 =	Y. 7 x 8 =
I. 9 x 12 =	' 4 x 4 =	Q. 5 x 5 =
B. 12 x 12 =	C. 10 x 10 =	P. 8 x 5 =

Why is multiplication so cool?

144 81 100 72 54 132 81   108 33 16 132   72

132 54 40 81 49   25 54 108 100 64   72 110 45

81 72 132 56   32 72 56   33 35   72 45 45

33 36 108 110 63 132   54 40 121

Division in Motion

 There are three parts to a division problem.

divisor
(number in each group)

$$4\overline{)12}\,^{3}$$

quotient *(number of groups)*

dividend *(total number)*

Divide.

A. $2\overline{)24}$ $3\overline{)9}$ $4\overline{)16}$ $6\overline{)12}$

B. $9\overline{)27}$ $6\overline{)42}$ $7\overline{)49}$ $4\overline{)24}$

C. $6\overline{)36}$ $8\overline{)40}$ $9\overline{)36}$ $6\overline{)24}$

D. $4\overline{)20}$ $3\overline{)27}$ $5\overline{)35}$ $7\overline{)84}$

E. $8\overline{)24}$ $9\overline{)45}$ $4\overline{)32}$ $3\overline{)18}$

F. $8\overline{)72}$ $5\overline{)25}$ $7\overline{)77}$ $6\overline{)30}$

G. $9\overline{)81}$ $4\overline{)32}$ $8\overline{)80}$ $7\overline{)28}$

Division Fireworks

Divide.

A. 70)‾490‾   90)‾300‾   40)‾322‾   30)‾150‾

B. 80)‾664‾   30)‾98‾   60)‾324‾   60)‾420‾

C. 70)‾498‾   50)‾154‾   80)‾165‾   90)‾550‾

D. 60)‾484‾   40)‾220‾   40)‾240‾   30)‾147‾   20)‾196‾

Let's Head 'Em Up and Move 'Em Out!

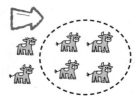  

4)6̄   *The **divisor** tells how many are in each group.*

$\frac{1}{4\overline{)6}}$ *The **quotient** tells how many groups there are.*

$\frac{1\,R2}{4\overline{)6}}$ *The **remainder** tells how many are left over.*

Circle to show each group. Write each quotient.

5)1̄3̄

7)1̄7̄

9)1̄1̄

3)7̄

8)1̄9̄

3)1̄0̄

4)‾13‾

6)‾8‾

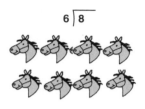

8)‾11‾

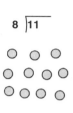

7)‾10‾

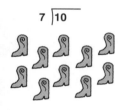

9)‾13‾

4)‾10‾

2)‾5‾

6)‾9‾

3)‾5‾

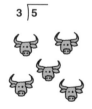

Number Stumper

Put ÷, x, +, or − in the boxes to make correct
math sentences.

1.

12		5		2	=9
2		6		4	=8
3		9		3	=4
=8		21		=11	

2.

8		5		4	=17
6		6		8	=28
15		21		9	=4
=29		=32		=23	

3.

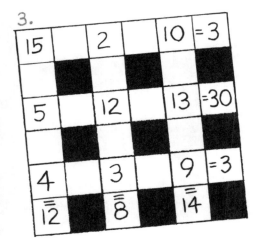

15		2		10	=3
	■		■		■
5		12		13	=30
	■		■		■
4		3		9	=3
=12	■	=8	■	=14	

4.

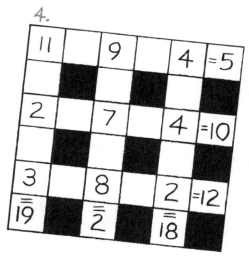

11		9		4	=5
	■		■		■
2		7		4	=10
	■		■		■
3		8		2	=12
=19	■	=2	■	=18	